Link 'N' Learn® Activity Book

By
Carol A. Thornton
and
Judith K. Wells

ISBN:1-56911-992-9
Printed in the United States of America.

Table of Contents

Introduction 5

Section One:
Exploration, 6–14

Teaching Notes 6-7
How Many Ways? 8
Make a Table 9
Train Links 10
Make a Train 11
A Flower Gathering 12
In and Out 13
Three Colors 14

Section Two:
Patterning, 15–23

Teaching Notes 15-16
Show It 17
Petal Patterns 18
Spiral Pattern 19
Make Patterns 20
What's in the Bag? 21
Border Story 22
Color a Pattern 23

Section Three:
Estimating & Comparing, 24–33

Teaching Notes 24-25
Color the Links 26
About How Many? 27
Guess and Count 28
Count On 29
Count Back 30
Five, More or Less 31
Start With/End With 32
In Order 33

Section Four:
Graphing & Probability, 34–43

Teaching Notes 34-35
Mud Piles 36
How Tall? 37
Graph a Link 38
Race to Snap 39
Spin and Tally 1 40
Spin and Tally 2 41
Predict, Draw, and Tally 42
What Will You Draw? 43

Section Five:
Estimating & Measuring, 44–52

Teaching Notes 44-45
Measure Me 46
All Around 47
Link Drop 48
About How Many Links? 49
All Around 50
How Many Links Long? 51
How Far? 52

Section Six:
Counting & Place Value 53–61

Teaching Notes 53-54

Chains and Links 55

Start With/End With 56

Puzzle Counts 57

Peephole Puzzles 58

What's Hidden? 59

In Order 60

Show Two Ways 61

Section Seven:
Addition 62–70

Teaching Notes 62-63

Tell a Bug Story 64

Flower Petals 65

Make Turnarounds 66

Count On   67

Ten or More Than Ten? 68

Pick a Pair 69

How Many? 70

Section Eight:
Subtraction 71–78

Teaching Notes 71-72

Tell a Story 73

Leaves on a Tree 74

Count Back 75

Compare Red and Blue Links 76

Check it Out 77

Take Away Some 78

Section Nine:
Multiplication & Division 79–85

Teaching Notes 79-80

Same to Each 81

Turnarounds 82

Sharing Bugs 83

Share Three Ways 84

Check It Out 85

Section Ten:
Fractions 86–88

Teaching Notes 86

Part are Red 87

Color a Chain 88

Teaching Aids 89-94

Spinners and a Ten-Frame 89-90

Hundreds Chart and Peephole Puzzles 91

Links 92-94

Bibliography 95-96

Introduction

With the *Link 'N' Learn®* Activity Book, teachers and parents can help children build their knowledge of early grade mathematics. The major concepts of the K-3 mathematics curriculum are presented in interesting ways that involve children in active learning through:

- Analyzing
- Exploration
- Problem Solving
- Working Cooperatively
- Communicating
- Predicting
- Representing
- Validating

Children are encouraged to manipulate the links while seeing, thinking about, and discussing the results of their activities.

Link 'N' Learn was rewritten in accordance with the NCTM's *Curriculum and Evaluation Standards for School Mathematics*. All activities and lessons follow the guidelines set for Grades K-3 mathematics. Special emphasis has been given to building mathematical communication, reasoning, connections, and problem solving.

The Link 'N' Learn Links

Link 'N' Learn links were developed in response the to need for children to learn mathematical concepts by manipulating concrete materials as well as through the interaction with peers and the environment. Links are brightly colored plastic pieces that easily snap together. Because links come in different colors and can be connected individually or in chain lengths, they can be used to show a variety of mathematical concepts. This book suggests ways to use links for teaching and learning mathematics in Grades K-3.

Lesson Organization

Link 'N' Learn is organized around the basic concepts and skills taught in the K-3 mathematics curriculum. Each lesson includes three parts:

- Getting Ready
- Basic Activity
- Extension

Complete *Teaching Notes* for each activity are provided at the beginning of each section. With the exception of the *Teaching Aids* (pages 89-94), each lesson is self-contained and only requires the use of links. Blackline masters of links in three sizes are provided in the *Teaching Aids* section. These can be colored and cut out for patterning, sequencing, and game activities. *Link 'N' Learn* activities can be integrated into your current mathematics instruction.

Materials Needed

Activities call for the use of *Rainbow Link 'N' Learn Links* (in 6 colors, LER 260) available from Learning Resources, Inc. However, it is possible to use this book with 4 color link sets. Notes for 4 color link sets are included in the teacher notes.

Introducing the Links

Children who have not had experiences with links will be interested and intrigued. They will want to touch and snap together the links. Provide time for free exploration before beginning formal instruction.

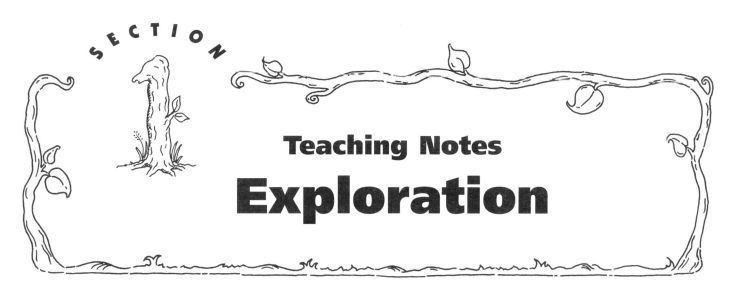

Teaching Notes
Exploration

Page 8: How Many Ways?

Objective: Make an organized list.

Getting Ready: Use one red, one blue, and one yellow link to arrange three different link chains. (RBY, RYB, BRY, BYR, YRB, YBR)

Basic Activity: For a party game, each child receives three links: one red, one orange (substitute yellow for orange if using 4-color links), and one green. How many different ways can the links be arranged? (6)

Place the links on the page, then color to show the arrangements.

Extension: Encourage children to make different arrangements with three links using two of the same color. For example: two reds and one blue. (RRB, RBR, BRR)

Page 9: Make a Table

Objective: Complete a table chart.

Getting Ready: Encourage children to make a red, red, green chain with their links.

Basic Activity: Children repeat a pattern to find the total for each color link. Children make a table showing chain lengths and colors.

Extension: Encourage children to make a green, red, red chain for Milli Millipedes' party. If there were ten red links in a birthday party chain with the green, red, red pattern, how many green links are there? (5) Encourage children to make a table to solve this problem.

Page 10: Train Links

Objective: Use logical reasoning.

Getting Ready: Children make three link chains of different lengths. Children compare trains and discuss lengths. Encourage them to arrange trains in order from shortest to longest.

Basic Activity: Children rank train sizes based on information given. Encourage children to use their trains from Getting Ready to complete the problem. (Track 1)

Extension: Ask children to complete this problem: The longest train is on Track 1. Track 3 has a train shorter than Track 2. Where is the shortest train? (Track 3)

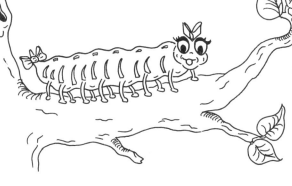

Link 'N' Learn® Activity Book
© Learning Resources, Inc.

Page 11: Make a Chain

Objective: Guess and check.

Getting Ready: Encourage children to make a red chain of six links, a green chain of four, a blue chain of two, a yellow chain of five, and an orange train of three. Place the chains on the activity page.

Basic Activity: Encourage children to find the sum of nine with their link chains. You might have them make a chain length of nine for comparison. (6 and 3, 4 and 5, or 4, 3, and 2.)

Extension: Challenge children to make chains of eight, ten, and eleven with the set lengths from the Basic Activity.

Page 12: A Flower Gathering

Objective: Act out a story, nonstandard addition.

Getting Ready: Two beetles (use blue links for beetles) crawled over to a leaf. Next, some grasshoppers (use green links for grasshoppers) hopped over to the same leaf. There were five bugs by the leaf. How many grasshoppers were there? Repeat this process using other insects, colors, and numbers.

Basic Activity: Three ladybugs (use red links for ladybugs) were crawling on a flower. Then some bumblebees (use yellow links for bumblebees) buzzed over to the flower. There were seven bugs around the flower. How many bumblebees were there? Encourage children to write a number sentence to describe the story.

Extension: Encourage children to make up a story of their own using links. They can challenge their peers to write a number sentence describing the story.

Page 13: In and Out

Objective: Act out a story, nonstandard addition.

Getting Ready: Encourage children to place a number of links in your hand (less than ten). Let some of the links fall without children seeing how many. Say: "There are four links left in my hand. How many fell?"

Basic Activity: Jerry put six links in a friend's hand. Some fell out. There were four links left in the friend's hand. How many links fell out? Repeat this process using various amounts.

Extension: Encourage children to make up their own story. They can challenge their peers to write a number sentence describing the story.

Page 14: Three Colors

Objective: Use logical reasoning.

Getting Ready: Children lay out three rows of links, each row in one color. Encourage children to discuss the colors and their arrangements.

Basic Activity: Jacki Junebug had three blue links, three red links, and three orange links (substitute orange for yellow if using 4-color links). She wanted to arrange them so she had one of each color in each row and column. Encourage children to arrange their links for her. Then color the arrangement. (One solution is: OBR, BRO, ROB)

Extension: Challenge children to make an arrangement using four colors with four rows and columns.

How Many Ways?

Use three links: red, orange, and green to make different arrangements. Find all the ways the links can be arranged. Color the links on the page to show your arrangements.

1.

2.

3.

4.

5.

6.

Link 'N' Learn® Activity Book
© Learning Resources, Inc.

Name _____ **Date** _____

Make a Table

Jesse and Rose hung a red, red, green pattern chain for Milli Millipede's birthday party. Jesse counted five green links. How many red links are there? _____

Complete the table below showing the number of red and green links.

Green Links	1	2	3	4	5
Red Links	2	4			

Train Links

Three trains come to the station. The shortest train is on Track 2. The Track 3 train is longer than the Track 1 train. What track is the middle-sized train on? _____

Use your links to help find the answer.

Make a Chain

Frankie Firefly wanted to make a chain with nine links to hang at Milli's party. He could pick from those pictured below. Which chains could he choose? _____ and _____.

2

3

4

5

6

A Flower Gathering

Listen to your teacher's stories and act them out with links. Write a number sentence to describe each story.

_____ + _____ = _____   _____ + _____ = _____

_____ + _____ = _____   _____ + _____ = _____

In and Out

Listen to your teacher's stories and act them out with links. Write a number sentence to describe each story.

_____ __ _____ _____   _____ __ _____ _____

_____ __ _____ _____   _____ __ _____ _____

Three Colors

Jacki Junebug wants to put three red, three orange, and three blue links in a box so that each row and column has one link of each color. Place and color the links below to show this pattern.

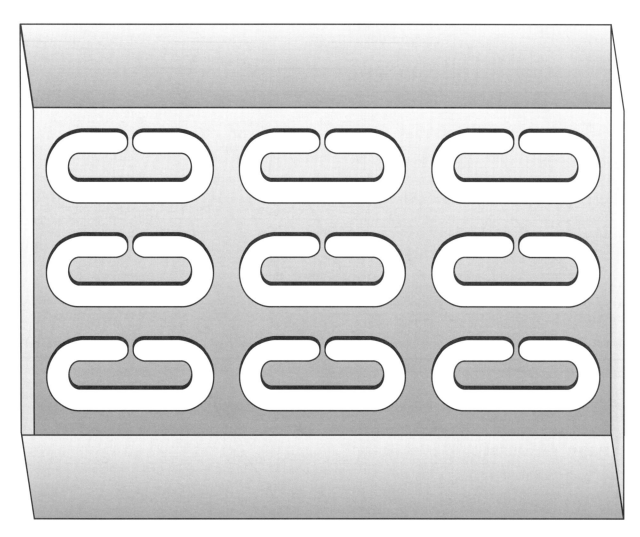

Link 'N' Learn® Activity Book
© Learning Resources, Inc.

SECTION 2

Teaching Notes
Patterning

Page 17: Show It

Objective: Act out and record a rhythm pattern.

Getting Ready: Make music for Antonio and Anita Ant to listen to in their garden. Clap your hands and slap your knees to form a rhythm pattern. Allow children to improvise by snapping their fingers and stomping their feet. Verbalize patterns such as: "clap, clap, clap, snap, snap, snap; a, a, a, b, b, b; 1, 1, 1, 2, 2, 2."

Basic Activity: Designate link colors as rhythm sounds. For example, a snap is red, a clap is blue, etc. Have children place links to show the pattern.

Extension: Encourage children to make different patterns with links and have peers act out the rhythm.

Page 18: Petal Patterns

Objective: Show and record color patterns.

Getting Ready: Encourage children to find patterns in your classroom.

Basic Activity: Children use two and three links to make petal patterns on a flower found in Antonio and Anita Ant's garden. Encourage children to discuss and share their patterns.

Extension: Children make new patterns by adding petals to flowers. Encourage them to make a second row of petals.

Page 19: Spiral Patterns

Objective: Create and record a color pattern.

Getting Ready: Go on a pattern hunt! Look for examples of patterns in nature. Shells, leaves, pine cones, and vegetables all have patterns.

Basic Activity: Show children examples of spiral patterns on shells. Encourage them to make a chain pattern and wrap it into a spiral. Color and record the pattern.

Extension: Display patterns children have found or made on a bulletin board. Discuss the differences and similarities in patterns.

Page 20: Make Patterns

Objective: See, copy, and extend a pattern.

Getting Ready: Encourage children to form a pattern chain. Elicit ways to describe the pattern.

Basic Activity: Make a pattern using links on Willis Worm (the first worm). Encourage children to continue the pattern on Wanda Worm (the second worm). Color to record the pattern.

Extension: Encourage children to start patterns for their peers to extend. Hang pattern chains about the room for children to extend.

Page 21: What's in the Bag?

Objective: Discover and extend patterns.

Getting Ready: Place a pattern chain in a bag. Slowly pull the chain out of the bag. Encourage children to guess what link should be next in the pattern. Keep track of predictions.

Basic Activity: Children make a pattern chain and hide it in a bag. One child slowly pulls out the chain while a partner tells what link should appear next. Color and record the pattern.

Extension: At different stations in your classroom, place bags containing pattern chains. At each station, ask one child to slowly pull out the chain one link at one time while the group predicts the next link. Record predictions then reveal the chain.

Page 22: Border Story

Objective: Make and record a border pattern.

Getting Ready: Encourage children to make a pattern train with their links. Other children have to continue the pattern. Join the ends of the train to make a continuous pattern; add more links as necessary.

Basic Activity: Children color the link pattern on the activity page. Then they write and describe their borders. Use words such as fence, corral, frame, and rectangle to describe the border.

Extension: Children share their descriptions with others. Classmates are challenged to model the border from the description. Match the new border to the old border to check.

Page 23: Color a Pattern

Objective: Matrix patterns.

Getting Ready: Make a matrix pattern for children to examine. Place two different links on the activity page. Repeat this pair to make new patterns. Ask children to describe the patterns.

Basic Activity: Children make their own matrix patterns on the activity page. Encourage them to color the pattern on the page. You may wish to have children describe their patterns in a paragraph.

Extension: Start a matrix pattern and challenge children to predict and extend the pattern.

Show It

Show a rhythm pattern with the links below. Color to record your pattern.

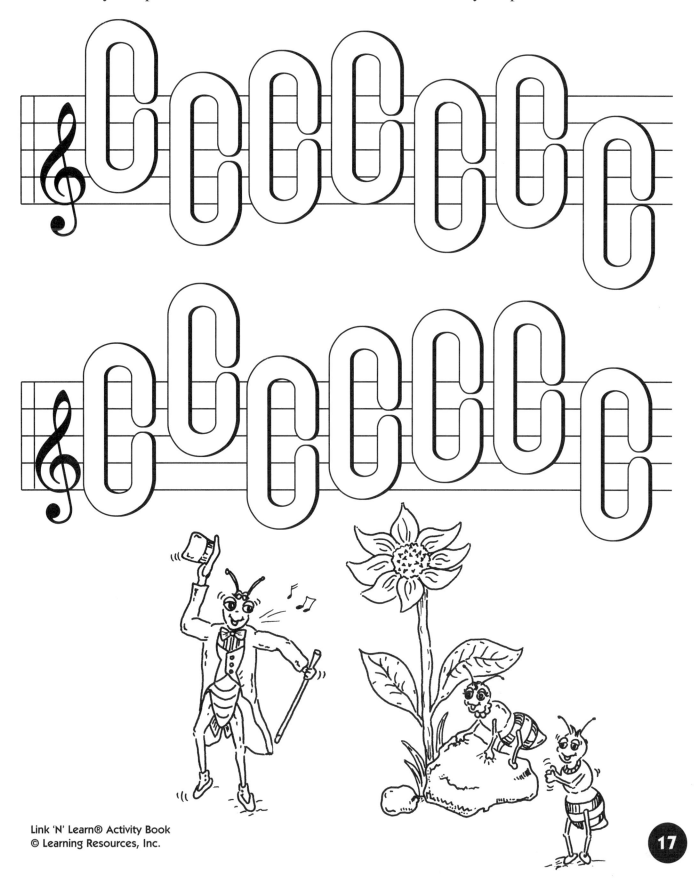

Petal Patterns

Place links on the petals to make a pattern on a flower planted in Antonio and Anita Ant's garden. Color to record.

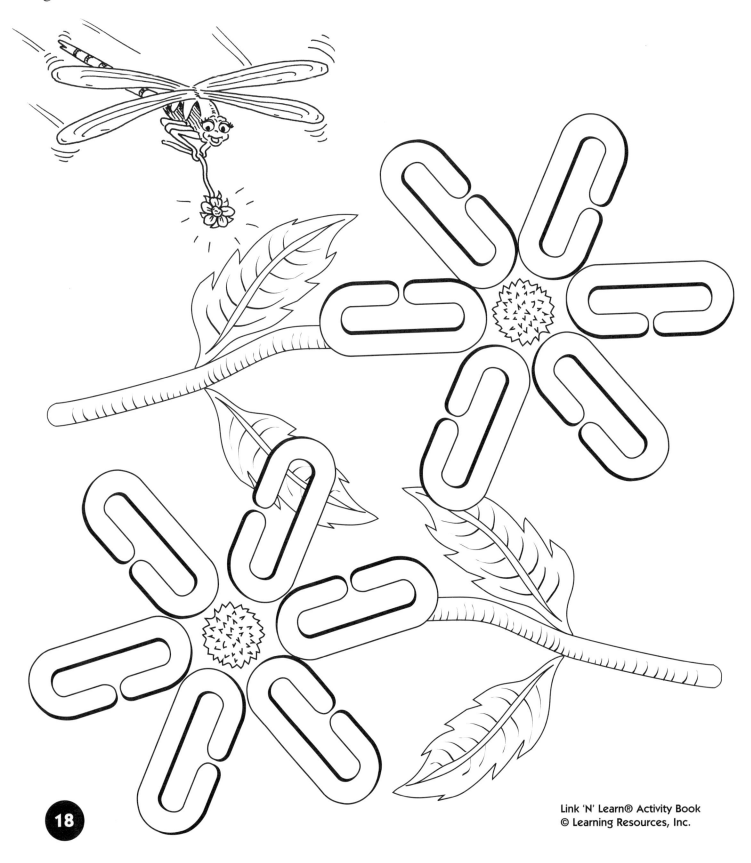

Spiral Patterns

Make a pattern chain and wrap it into a spiral. Color your pattern below.

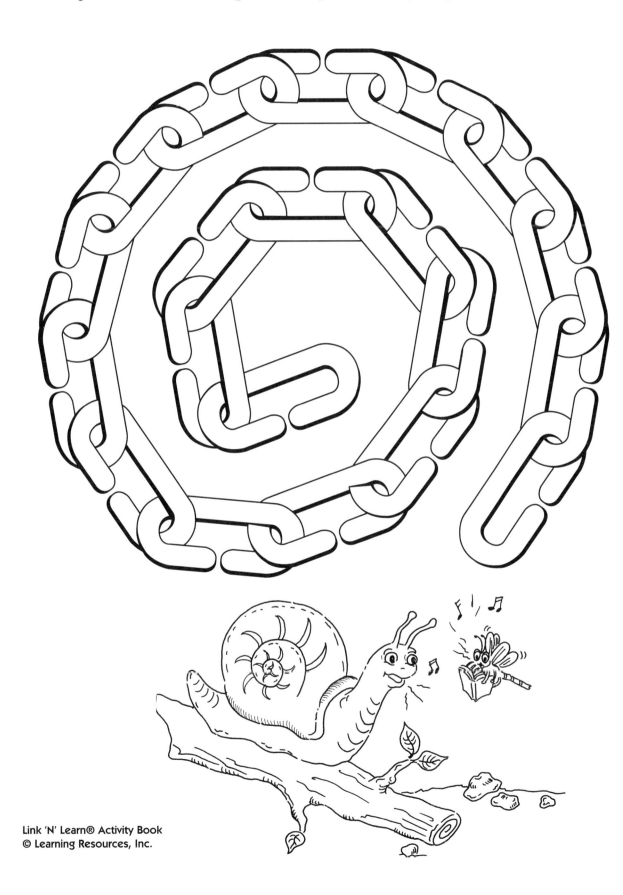

Make Patterns

Make a pattern on Willis and Wanda Worm using pairs of links. Color your pattern below.

What's in the Bag?

Make a chain pattern and hide it in a bag. Pull the chain out slowly and have a partner guess the pattern. Color the pattern below.

Border Story

Create a square border with 6 links on each side. Write a paragraph describing your border. Color your pattern below.

Link 'N' Learn® Activity Book
© Learning Resources, Inc.

Color a Pattern

Start a pattern with links. Encourage a partner to finish your pattern.

Teaching Notes
Estimating & Comparing

Page 26: Color the Links

Objective: Ordinal numbers.

Getting Ready: Children count as they cover each link on the page. Ask: "Do any of the rows have the same number?"

Basic Activity: Use words such as: first, second, third, and last to direct children to color the links.

Extension: Ask children to explain why one row has more links than another when all the rows are close to the same length.

Page 27: About How Many?

Objective: Estimate and count to check numbers to twenty.

Getting Ready: Show children a necklace made of links. Ask them to estimate how many links are in the necklace.

Basic Activity: Children make objects with links then estimate and count the number of links.

Extension: Ask children to link two of the objects together and find the sum of the links.

Page 28: Guess and Count

Objective: Estimate, count, and record in a bar graph.

Getting Ready: Children grab a handful of links. They estimate and then count the links.

Basic Activity: Children grab a handful of links and challenge a friend to estimate, then count how many links there are. Children record the data in a chart. Encourage children to repeat the exercise and discuss strategies used in estimating the number of links in the piles.

Extension: Encourage partners to each grab a pile of links, then compare the piles and estimate which has more or less.

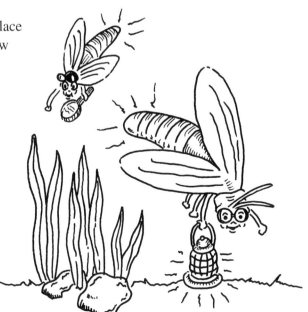

Page 29: Count On

Objective: Counting on 1, 2, or 3.

Getting Ready: Show children how to use a pencil and a paper clip as a spinner. Demonstrate a few problems on the overhead using the spinner and links.

Basic Activity: One child places some fireflies (use red links as fireflies) on the jar and says the total. Another spins the spinner and counts on. Repeat with other starting numbers.

Extension: Encourage children to write number sentences describing their counting on problems.

Page 30: Count Back

Objective: Counting back with 1, 2, and 3.

Getting Ready: Encourage children to make a chain of seven links and count back one-by-one as they remove the links.

Basic Activity: Children imagine that links are flies (use purple links as flies, blue if you're using 4-color links). Encourage children to take a handful of flies and place them on Spiffy Spider's web. Ask them to find the total, spin a spinner, and count back. Repeat with new handfuls.

Extension: Write a number on the board and hold up 1, 2, or 3 fingers. Encourage children to count back.

Page 31: Five, More or Less

Objective: Estimating, using five as a benchmark.

Getting Ready: Put a pencil on the overhead with links attached to either side. Ask: "Which side has more links?" Match the links one-to-one to check.

Basic Activity: Children lay out a pile of links and estimate using five as a benchmark. Encourage children to use the five frame. Children should write sentences such as "7 is more than 5" or "3 is less than 5."

Extension: Repeat the exercise using a ten frame.

Page 32: Start With/End With

Objective: One more or one less.

Getting Ready: Hang chains next to each other that have a difference of one or two links. Count the longer or shorter chain and derive the length of the other.

Basic Activity: Children take turns finding totals using handfuls of links and a spinner.

Extension: Encourage children to start with a number and tell how the spinner will land. Then add or subtract. Use links to check.

Page 33: In Order

Objective: Order numbers under twenty.

Getting Ready: Hang different length chains and have children put them in order from shortest to longest. Children should then count the number of links and record them in order.

Basic Activity: Children write numbers from smallest to largest.

Extension: Encourage children to fill in the numbers between the numbers they wrote.

Color the Links

Listen to your teacher's directions, then color the links.

About How Many?

Make the chains. Guess how many links are in each chain. Record your guess. Then count to see the results.

Necklace | My Guess _____ (number of links)
My Count _____ (number of links)

Belt | My Guess _____ (number of links)
My Count _____ (number of links)

Crown | My Guess _____ (number of links)
My Count _____ (number of links)

Bracelet | My Guess _____ (number of links)
My Count _____ (number of links)

Guess and Count

Put a pile of links on your desk. Ask a friend to guess how many links there are. Record the guess. Then count to check. Record the actual total. Make a new pile of links after each table is filled.

Guess										
Count										

Guess										
Count										

Guess										
Count										

Guess										
Count										

Guess										
Count										

Link 'N' Learn® Activity Book
© Learning Resources, Inc.

Name _____ Date _____

Count On

Pretend that your red links are fireflies. Put some fireflies in the jar and count the total. Spin and add that many more fireflies to the jar. Count on to find the total.

Count Back

Pretend that your purple links are flies. Place some flies on Spiffy Spider's web. Spin and take away that many flies from the web. Count back to find the total.

Link 'N' Learn® Activity Book
© Learning Resources, Inc.

Five, More or Less

Lay out some links. Are there more than five? Less than five? Use the five frame to check. Write a sentence describing your total.

_____

_____

Name _____ **Date** _____

Start With/End With

Grab a handful of links. Count the links. Record the total under the "Start" side of the table. Spin and add that many more. Write the new total under the "End" side of the table.

1 more

2 less

1 less

2 more

START

END

Link 'N' Learn® Activity Book
© Learning Resources, Inc.

In Order

Write the numbers in order from smallest to largest. Use your link chains to check.

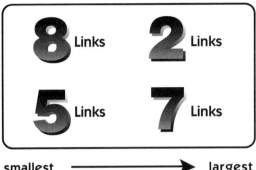

8 Links 2 Links
5 Links 7 Links

smallest ——————➤ largest

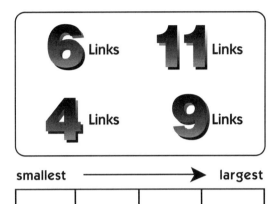

6 Links 11 Links
4 Links 9 Links

smallest ——————➤ largest

2 Links 9 Links
12 Links 5 Links

smallest ——————➤ largest

4 Links 2 Links
12 Links 3 Links

smallest ——————➤ largest

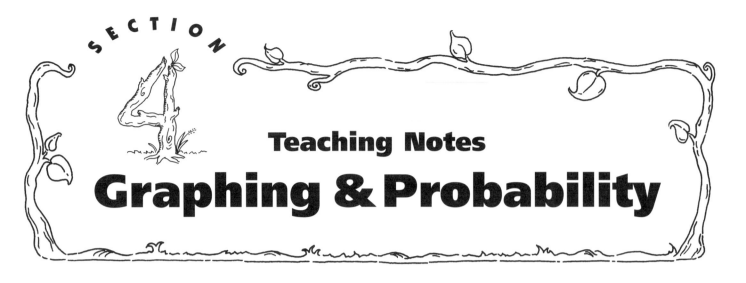

SECTION 4

Teaching Notes
Graphing & Probability

Page 36: Mud Piles

Objective: Predict and record results in a table.

Getting Ready: Draw a mud pile on the overhead. Drop links over the mud pile. Encourage children to discuss where they landed. Listen to children's descriptions.

Basic Activity: Children drop links over Willis and Wanda Worm's mud pile and record where they landed. Encourage children to write a paragraph describing the results of their experiment.

Extension: Use different size mud piles and discuss the results.

Page 37: How Tall?

Objective: Tally and graph.

Getting Ready: Encourage children to estimate smaller objects before estimating your height. Have them estimate the height of a desk or a chair or a table. Then they can use that height to estimate your height.

Basic Activity: Record and tally children's estimates for the height. Find out what most children guessed. Then measure the height. Count and record the total number of links.

Extension: Children can guess and measure their own heights.

Page 38: Graph a Link

Objective: Complete a bar graph.

Getting Ready: Form a chain of several colors. Discuss which color is the most, least, etc.

Basic Activity: Children grab a handful of links and record in a bar graph how many they grabbed. Children should label the axes by coloring the links and finishing the numbering.

Extension: Repeat the experiment. Vary the number of colors in the population. Encourage children to compare and discuss their graphs.

Page 39: Race to Snap

Objective: Complete and compare information in a bar graph.

Getting Ready: Ask children how long they think it would take you to make a chain of fifteen links. Discuss varying lengths of chains and time to make them.

Basic Activity: Children time each other to see how many links long they can make a chain in one minute. Children graph the results.

Extension: Challenge children to find the fewest and most links snapped.

Page 40: Spin and Tally 1

Objective: Use a spinner and record outcomes.

Getting Ready: Have each child color the links on the spinner a different color. If you are using only 4-color links, leave the remaining two links uncolored as free spins. Challenge children to tell you what the possible outcomes are.

Basic Activity: Children spin and tally the color. They stop when they get five tallies of one color.

Extension: Make a class data chart from each child's data. Discuss the results. You should have the same probability for each color.

Page 41: Spin and Tally 2

Objective: Use a spinner and record outcomes.

Getting Ready: Have each child color the links on the spinner. If you are using only 4-color links, leave the remaining two links uncolored as free spins. Challenge children to tell you what the possible outcomes are.

Basic Activity: Children spin and tally the color. They stop when they get ten tallies for one color.

Extension: Make a class data chart from each child's data. Discuss the results. You should have the same probability for each color. You might want to discuss what happens when you use a biased spinner.

Page 42: Predict, Draw, and Tally

Objective: Experimental probability by determining colors in a bag.

Getting Ready: Put a handful of links in a bag. Discuss the possibilities for pulling a certain color link.

Basic Activity: Each child draws a link from the bag and records the color on their data table. Stop when one color has ten tallies.

Extension: Discuss what happens if you replace or choose not to replace the link you drew from the bag.

Page 43: What Will You Draw?

Objective: Experimental probability with replacement.

Getting Ready: Put a handful of links in a bag. Discuss the possibilities for pulling a certain color link.

Basic Activity: Encourage children to predict the colors they will pull based on data collected.

Extension: Challenge students to explain why they drew more of one color than another and vice versa.

Mud Piles

Drop a link over Willis and Wanda Worm's mud pile. Watch where the link lands. Record in the table where the link landed. Drop two more links and record where they land. Write a paragraph describing the results.

Where the Links Fell

	Trial 1	Trial 2	Trial 3
IN			
OUT			
ON			

_____

_____

_____

_____

Link 'N' Learn® Activity Book
© Learning Resources, Inc.

How Tall?

How many links tall is your teacher? Keep track of the guesses made by some partners. Then measure the height.

Less than 20 Links	21 - 40 Links	41 - 60 Links	More than 60 Links
Partner 1			
Partner 2			
Partner 3			
Partner 4			
Partner 5			

Most Guessed Links_____

My teacher is _____links tall.

Graph a Link

Grab a handful of links. Make a graph showing how many of each color links you grabbed. Fill in the missing numbers on the graph.

1   2   3   ▲   5   6   7   8   ▲   10   11   12

Name _____ Date _____

Race to Snap

Snap together as many links as you can in one minute. Record your results. Test your friend's speed and record the results. Make and label a graph.

Less than 10 Links												
11 to 20 Links												
21 to 30 Links												
More than 30 Links	1	2	3	4	5	6	7	8	9	10	11	12

Partner Number

Most links snapped in a minute: _____

Fewest links snapped in a minute: _____

Name _____ Date _____

Spin and Tally 1

Color the links on the spinner red, green, yellow, blue, orange, and purple. Spin and tally the color. Stop when one color has a total of five.

Tally

Red	
Green	
Yellow	
Blue	
Orange	
Purple	

Spin and Tally 2

Color the links on the spinner red, green, yellow, blue, orange, and purple. Predict what will happen when you spin and keep track of your colors. Stop when one color has a total of ten.

Tally

Red	
Green	
Yellow	
Blue	
Orange	
Purple	

Predict, Draw, and Tally

Put a handful of links in a bag. Predict the color you will draw. Draw one link from the bag and record its color. Stop when one color has ten tallies.

Link Tally

Red

Green

Yellow

Blue

Orange

Purple

Link 'N' Learn® Activity Book
© Learning Resources, Inc.

What Will You Draw?

Put a large handful of links in a bag. Predict the color you will draw. Stop when one color has ten tallies. Place the links back in the bag. Predict which color has the most links in the bag and which has the least. Count to check.

Link Tally

Red	
Green	
Yellow	
Blue	
Orange	
Purple	

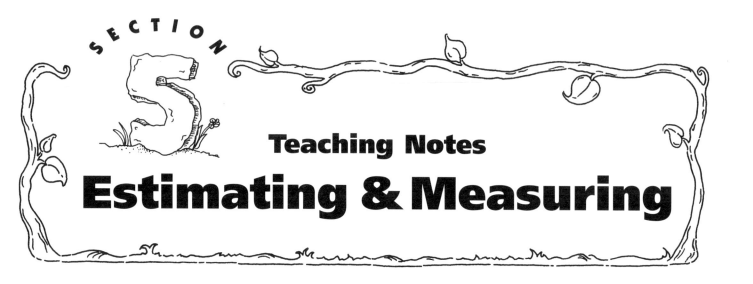

Teaching Notes
Estimating & Measuring

Page 46: Measure Me

Objective: Estimate and measure body lengths in links.

Getting Ready: Ask children to predict and estimate the number of links necessary to extend from their wrist to their elbow. Use links to check.

Basic Activity: Children work with a partner and measure body parts with links.

Extension: Ask children to find the longest and shortest body part. Challenge them to find similarities in measurements.

Page 47: All Around

Objective: Children find informal perimeters.

Getting Ready: Encourage children to make a design with links and have a partner estimate the number of links in the design.

Basic Activity: Children estimate the number of links necessary to measure around the car on the page. Then they measure to see. Discuss possible numbers for measuring real cars.

Extension: Encourage students to estimate lengths of objects in the classroom.

Page 48: Link Drop

Objective: Estimate distances between links.

Getting Ready: Model the exercise on the overhead projector for children to copy.

Basic Activity: Children drop two links, estimate, and measure the distance between their landing positions.

Extension: Encourage children to relate lengths in links to lengths in centimeters. Discuss their methods and strategies.

Page 49: About How Many Links?

Objective: Estimate the length of objects in links.

Getting Ready: Hold up a chain of five links and challenge children to use five as an anchor to estimate the number of links necessary to measure the span of a door in your classroom.

Basic Activity: Children estimate lengths then fasten links together to measure the objects shown that are found in your classroom.

Extension: Encourage children to look for lengths in the classroom that are equivalent to the objects they measured during the activity.

Page 50: All Around

Objective: Estimate lengths and perimeters.

Getting Ready: Fence in the overhead projector screen with links and ask children to count the links.

Basic Activity: Encourage children to estimate lengths around objects with links. Then, have them measure.

Extension: Challenge children to discover the discrepancy between laying links side-by-side and end-to-end. Encourage them to measure a perimeter both ways and to discuss their results.

Page 51: How Many Links Long?

Objective: Estimate and measure lengths.

Getting Ready: Place a length of masking tape on the chalkboard. Ask children to find an object in the classroom that has an equivalent length, then measure it with links.

Basic Activity: Place eight strips of masking tape (various lengths) about the classroom. Label them A-H. Encourage children to estimate the lengths and then measure.

Extension: Have children compare measurements taken with links to those taken with a ruler.

Page 52: How Far?

Objective: Estimate, then use links to check distances between objects.

Getting Ready: Make a ten-link as an anchor for children to make comparisons. Repeat for chains of 20 or 30.

Basic Activity: Draw a long horizontal line on the chalkboard. Write the letters A-F on the line at various distances and encourage children to estimate the lengths between different points. Discuss patterns and strategies.

Extension: Ask children to make a 25-link chain and estimate the points at which it will pass through when placed at certain locations on the line.

Measure Me

Guess the lengths in links it takes to measure parts of your body. Record your guess. Then measure to find out.

How many links do you think it takes to measure?

		Guess	Measure
A	Around your head		
B	From neck to wrist		
C	From neck to waist		
D	Around your wrist		
E	Around your waist		
F	Around your ankle		
G	The length of your foot		
H	From waist to foot		

Link 'N' Learn® Activity Book
© Learning Resources, Inc.

All Around

Guess the lengths in links it takes to measure around the car. Then measure to find out.

Link Drop

Hold two links by your waist. Drop them. How far apart did they land? Record your guess, then measure the distance with links.

How Far Apart?

Drop	My Guess	My Measure
1		
2		
3		
4		
5		
6		
7		
8		
9		
10		

Link 'N' Learn® Activity Book
© Learning Resources, Inc.

About How Many Links?

Find the lengths with links. Estimate, then measure the objects below that are found in your classroom.

A Chair Leg

My estimate _____

My count _____

The Long Side of a Table

My estimate _____

My count _____

A Table Leg

My estimate _____

My count _____

The Length of a Book

My estimate _____

My count _____

All Around

Find the lengths with links. Estimate, then measure the objects below that are found in your classroom.

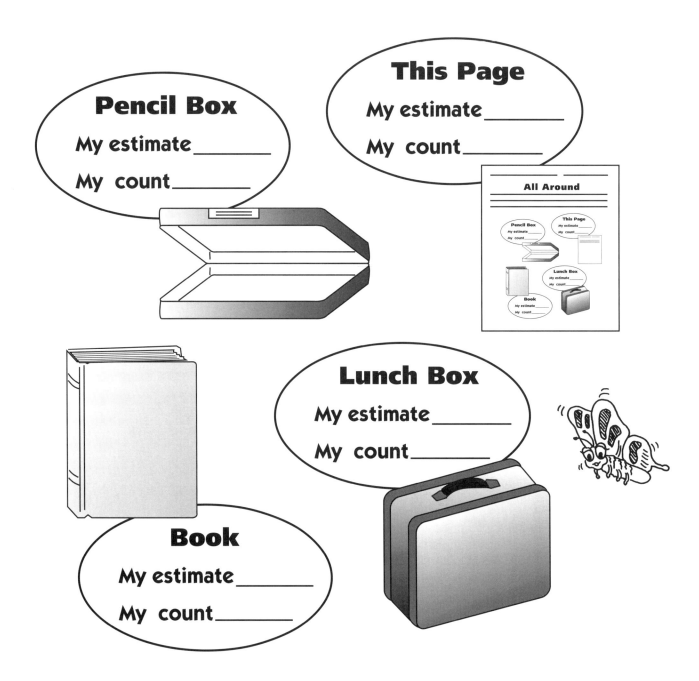

Pencil Box

My estimate_____

My count_____

This Page

My estimate_____

My count_____

Lunch Box

My estimate_____

My count_____

Book

My estimate_____

My count_____

Name _____ Date _____

How Many Links Long?

Guess, then measure each tape's length with links. Record your guess and measurement in the table below. How many links will it take?

How Many Will It Take?

Tape	My Guess	My Measure
A		
B		
C		
D		
E		
F		
G		
H		

Name _____ Date _____

How Far?

Estimate and measure each length drawn on the chalkboard. Use a ten-link chain to help you estimate.

How Far?

Distance	My Estimate	My Measure
A to B		
A to C		
B to D		
C to E		
D to F		

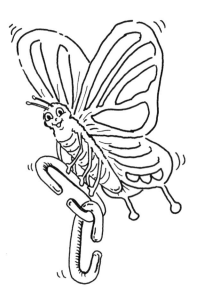

SECTION 6

Teaching Notes
Counting & Place Value

Page 55: Chains and Links

Objective: Write a two-digit number shown by links.

Getting Ready: Encourage children to make a single digit number with links on a ten frame (page 90).

Basic Activity: Children match links to the picture then write the number of links shown.

Extension: Help children learn numerical values by challenging them to place a star beside numbers that are greater than 50. Excelled children can order the numbers.

Page 56: Start With/End With

Objective: Write one or two more than or less than a number.

Getting Ready: Encourage children to use a book's page numbers to order numbers and subtract or add one or two.

Basic Activity: Give children a starting number. Children spin a spinner and add or subtract one or two to give a new number.

Extension: Challenge children to make a chain of numbers. Start with a number, spin the spinner, add or subtract one or two, then take the resulting number and spin again.

Page 57: Puzzle Counts

Objective: Count on by tens or ones with a hundreds chart (page 91).

Getting Ready: Introduce children to the hundreds chart (page 91). Discuss number order, especially where to go after ten. (Down to the next line, like when children are reading.)

Basic Activity: Children take a starting number, add links, and use the hundreds chart as a guide to complete the movements shown on the activity page. Children then record their answers.

Extension: Repeat the same activity, but count backwards to the starting number.

Page 58: Peephole Puzzles

Objective: Copy a two-digit number and write numbers by adding or subtracting ten or one.

Getting Ready: Cover up one number on the overhead and encourage children to find the surrounding numbers on a hundreds chart using links.

Basic Activity: Place a peephole puzzle over a number on the hundreds chart and ask children to find the surrounding numbers by adding or subtracting ten or one.

Extension: Use the peephole puzzle B (page 91) to challenge children to find new numbers.

Page 59: What's Hidden?

Objective: Identify missing ten chains and ones to represent a number.

Getting Ready: Place links and tell children, "I have three chains (of ten) and eight links in the bag." Ask: "How many links are in the bag?" Repeat for other chains and links.

Basic Activity: Children show each number with chains and links, then determine which chains and links are hiding.

Extension: One child takes chains and links, then drops them into a bag. Another child tells the number in the bag.

Page 60: In Order

Objective: Order two-digit numbers.

Getting Ready: Write some two-digit numbers on the board. Ask children to model the numbers with links and arrange them in order.

Basic Activity: Children model numbers with links and write them in order from smallest to largest.

Extension: Encourage children to write in order the numbers between the numbers they arranged.

Page 61: Show Two Ways

Objective: Rename two-digit numbers.

Getting Ready: Distribute copies of page 94 to children. Write the number 25 on the board and ask children to cut out 25 loose links. Encourage them to group the links in fives and tens.

Basic Activity: Children arrange links to show a number, then they record the number.

Extension: Challenge children to find other ways to show the numbers on the activity page.

Chains and Links

Match the links in each picture. Find the total and write it in the box to the right.

1.

2.

3.

4.

Start With/End With

Take some link chains. Estimate and count the total. Write the total in the table below. Spin and add or subtract as directed. Write the new total in the table.

1 more	2 less
1 less	2 more

START	END

Link 'N' Learn® Activity Book
© Learning Resources, Inc.

Puzzle Counts

Use a hundreds chart to do the following puzzles. Use links to check your answers.

1. START
26

2. START
49

3. START
64

4. START
38

5. START
58

6. START
79

Peephole Puzzles

Use a hundreds chart and links to complete these peephole puzzles.

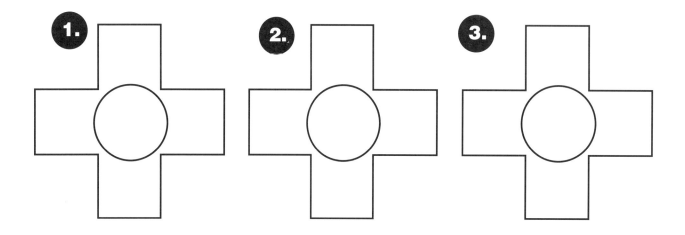

1.

2.

3.

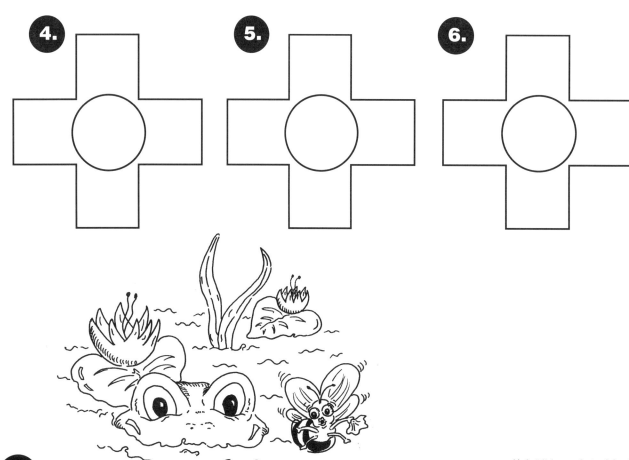

4.

5.

6.

Name _____ Date _____

What's Hidden?

Use ten chains and links to show each number. Find out what's hidden.

1. **38 in all.**

What's hidden?
_____ tens
_____ ones

2. **43 in all.**

What's hidden?
_____ tens
_____ ones

3. **25 in all.**

What's hidden?
_____ tens
_____ ones

4. **52 in all.**

What's hidden?
_____ tens
_____ ones

In Order

Write the numbers in order from smallest to largest. Use link chains to check.

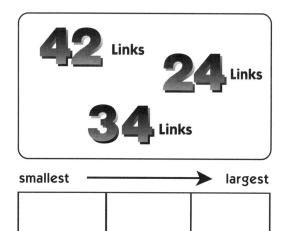

smallest ⟶ largest

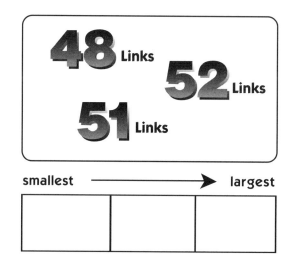

smallest ⟶ largest

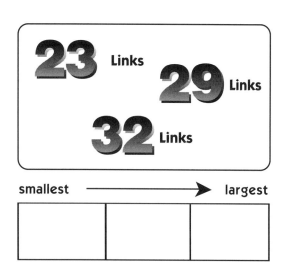

smallest ⟶ largest

Choose your own numbers.

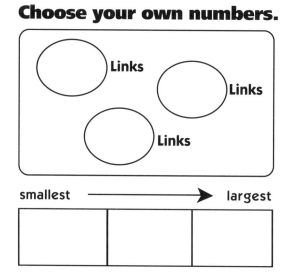

smallest ⟶ largest

Link 'N' Learn® Activity Book
© Learning Resources, Inc.

Name _____ **Date** _____

Show Two Ways

Write in the number shown with links. Show another way to make the number using links.

1.

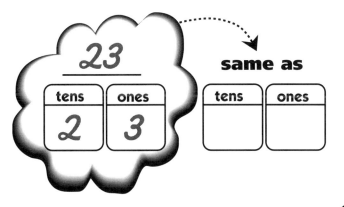

same as

tens	ones
2	3

tens	ones

2.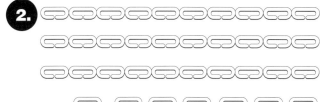

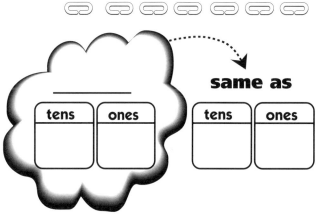

same as

_____

tens	ones

tens	ones

3.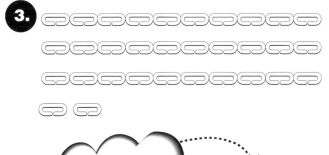

same as

_____

tens	ones

tens	ones

4.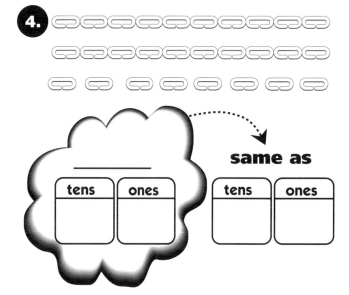

same as

_____

tens	ones

tens	ones

Teaching Notes
Counting & Place Value

Page 64: Tell a Bug Story

Objective: Addition concept, acting out an addition story.

Getting Ready: Tell addition stories to children and ask them to act them out with links. For example: "Two water bugs went for a swim. Three others decided to join them. How many water bugs went swimming?"

Basic Activity: Encourage children to tell and model addition stories with links.

Extension: Tell an addition story where no action occurred. For example: "Four water bugs had on red caps and four had on blue caps. How many water bugs had on caps?"

Page 65: Flower Petals

Objective: Breaking down five.

Getting Ready: Children take five links of 2 colors and attach them to their fingers. They open their hands to show a flower bloom. A peer writes a number sentence describing the bloom.

Basic Activity: Children use 2 colors of links to explore addends of the number five. Discuss zero as an addend.

Extension: Encourage children to make flowers with six or more petals and write number sentences to describe them.

Page 66: Make Turnarounds

Objective: Commutative property.

Getting Ready: Have children make chains with 2 colors showing a sum of four. Write addition sentences for the chains. Turn the chain upside down and write the turnaround sentence.

Basic Activity: Children make chains and write number sentences. They turn their chains around and write the turnaround sentence. For example: $3 + 2 = 5$ and $2 + 3 = 5$.

Extension: Make a bulletin board showing turnaround sentences for sums of four, five, six, seven, and eight. Discuss patterns.

Page 67: Count On

Objective: Addition facts having one, two, or three as an addend.

Getting Ready: Tell a story and ask children to model it with links. For example: "I saw a bunch of ants crawling up an ant hill. I counted nine. Then I saw three more. Count on with me. 9, 10, 11, 12."

Basic Activity: Children pick a number and count on.

Extension: Encourage children to count on using a book's page numbers.

Page 68: Ten or More Than Ten?

Objective: Making a ten.

Getting Ready: Encourage children to use 2 colors of links and find addends that make a ten on a ten frame. Write number sentences to record their findings.

Basic Activity: Children do only those problems which have a sum of ten.

Extension: Children show why the other problems do not have a sum of ten using links as a model.

Page 69: Pick a Pair

Objective: Two-digit addition.

Getting Ready: Encourage children to model two-digit numbers you write on the chalkboard with links.

Basic Activity: Children identify numbers using ten chains of links. They then create addition problems with the numbers. Encourage children to model and check their sums with links.

Extension: Challenge children to add three numbers with links as a model.

Page 70: How Many?

Objective: Model and record two-digit addition.

Getting Ready: One child takes a handful of links and groups them into tens and ones. Record the number. Another child repeats the exercise. They then find the sum of their links trading ones for ten chains if necessary.

Basic Activity: Children add numbers using links. Ten chains are made as numbers are grouped and arranged.

Extension: Encourage children to estimate sums before completing addition problems.

Tell a Bug Story

Use red links to help write and act out addition stories about water bugs. Write and act out an addition story for each number sentence.

For example: 4 water bugs + 2 water bugs = 6 water bugs.

3 + 2 = _____ water bugs   6 + 3 = _____ water bugs   4 + 3 = _____ water bugs

2 + 5 = _____ water bugs   1 + 7 = _____ water bugs   2 + 6 = _____ water bugs

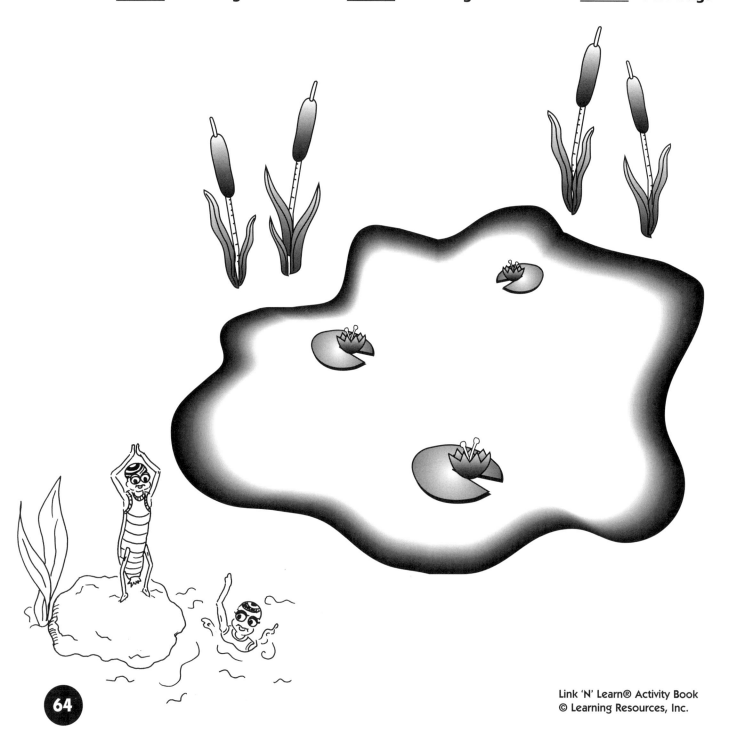

Flower Petals

Use links of two colors. Cover the petals. Write number sentences to show sums of five.

____ + ____ = **5**   ____ + ____ = **5**   ____ + ____ = **5**

____ + ____ = **5**   ____ + ____ = **5**   ____ + ____ = **5**

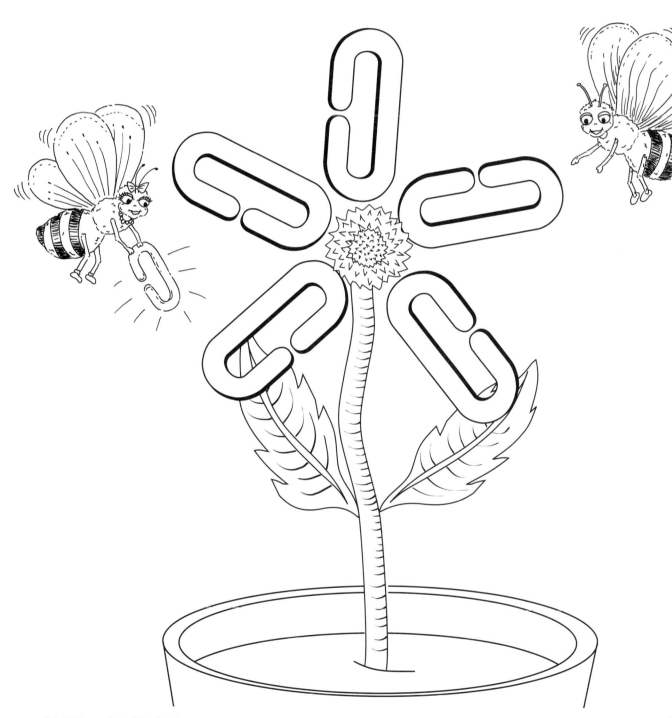

Make Turnarounds

Make two chains using two different colors. Put the two together and write a number sentence. Turn the chain upside down and write a new sentence.

Red Links   ## Yellow Links

$+$

Green Links

Orange Links

$+$

Turnaround

$+$ $+$

Turnaround

$+$ $+$

Link 'N' Learn® Activity Book
© Learning Resources, Inc.

Name _____ Date _____

Count On

Choose a number and write it in the box below. Count on. Write the sum.

[ ] + ⬭⬭⬭ → ___ + **3** = ___

[ ] + ⬭⬭ → ___ + **2** = ___

[ ] + ⬭⬭⬭ → ___ + **3** = ___

[ ] + ⬭⬭ → ___ + **2** = ___

Ten or More Than Ten?

Do the problems that make a ten. Use the 10-Frame and links to help.

10 - Frame

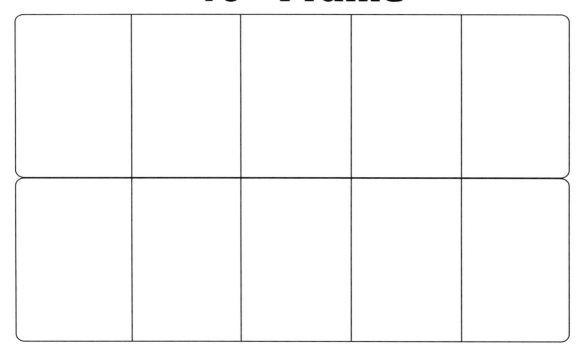

8 + 6	7 + 3	7 + 5	8 + 2	7 + 4	4 + 6
☐	☐	☐	☐	☐	☐

Link 'N' Learn® Activity Book
© Learning Resources, Inc.

Pick a Pair

Write the number for each group of links. Pick pairs and add.

34

	tens	ones
+		

	tens	ones
+		

	tens	ones
+		

	tens	ones
+		

	tens	ones
+		

	tens	ones
+		

Name _____ **Date** _____

How Many?

Grab a handful of links. Make ten-chains and record the total.

When you have 10 links, make a chain.

tens	ones
+	

tens	ones
+	

tens	ones
+	

tens	ones
+	

tens	ones
+	

tens	ones
+	

Link 'N' Learn® Activity Book
© Learning Resources, Inc.

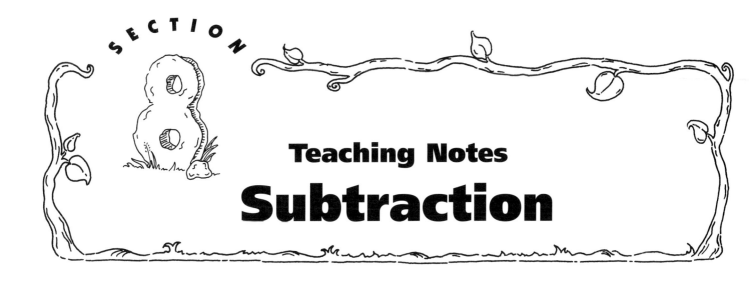

Teaching Notes
Subtraction

Page 73: Tell a Story

Objective: Subtraction, acting out a subtraction story.

Getting Ready: Tell subtraction stories to children and use links to act them out. For example: "Four ants crawled to get some crumbs left on a picnic blanket. Two became full and crawled away. How many ants were still eating the crumbs?"

Basic Activity: Encourage children to share and act out stories about ants of their own using the number sentences as a guide.

Extension: Tell stories without action. For example: "I saw seven butterflies on the blanket. Four were red, the rest were yellow. How many were yellow?"

Page 74: Leaves on a Tree

Objective: Subtraction, model, and record.

Getting Ready: Ask children to take 6 links and separate them into two piles to discover addends.

Basic Activity: Ask children to write number sentences describing falling leaves. Discuss zero and its meaning: $6 - 0 = 6$, no leaves were falling.

Extension: Encourage children to make trees with seven leaves and to write number sentences.

Page 75: Count Back

Objective: Subtracting 1, 2, or 3.

Getting Ready: Help children become accustomed to counting back by demonstrating problems on a number line.

Basic Activity: Encourage children to write the numbers as they count back. For example: "11– 3 is 11, 10, 9, 8."

Extension: Children can count backwards using numbers on the pages of books. Their peers can name a number in a book, then have them count back 1, 2, or 3 pages. Use the book to check.

Page 76: Compare Red and Purple Links

Objective: Subtracting 1, 2, or 3

Getting Ready: Two children take links and make two chains. They should compare the lengths and state which is greater and less than. Encourage them to find the difference in length between the chains.

Basic Activity: Children compare lengths of red and purple chains (substitiute blue for purple if using 4-color links). Encourage them to write which has more and to find the difference between the chains.

Extension: Encourage children to each grab a handful of links from a bag. They should compare the links and find the difference between the handfuls.

Page 77: Check It Out

Objective: Add to check.

Getting Ready: Give children a sample story to act out. For example: "There were eight cars in a train. The engineer unhooked two cars and towed them away. How many cars were still there?"

Basic Activity: Children make trains with links, then take some away. They write a subtraction sentence, then replace the links. Children check their work with an addition sentence.

Extension: Make a Subtraction Fact bulletin board with addition facts as hints or checks.

Page 78: Take Away Some

Objective: Two-digit subtraction.

Getting Ready: Give children a number and have them model it with links. Encourage them to use ten-link chains and ones to reinforce place value.

Basic Activity: Give children two two-digit numbers to subtract. Work with them as they model the numbers with links and make trades as necessary. Teach the algorithm after children are capable of modeling with links.

Extension: Children work together on problems to determine if they need to break a ten chain to solve the problem.

Link 'N' Learn® Activity Book
© Learning Resources, Inc.

Tell a Story

Use orange links to write and act out subtraction stories about ants for the number sentences below. For example: 4 ants – 2 ants = 2 ants.

7 – 3 = _____ants   6 – 2 = _____ants   7 – 5 = _____ants

6 – 4 = _____ ants   8 – 3 = _____ants   6 – 3 = _____ants

Leaves on a Tree

Count the leaves. Then let some fall to the ground. Write number sentences.

6 – _____ = _____leaves   6 – _____ = _____leaves

6 – _____ = _____leaves   6 – _____ = _____leaves

6 – _____ = _____leaves   6 – _____ = _____leaves

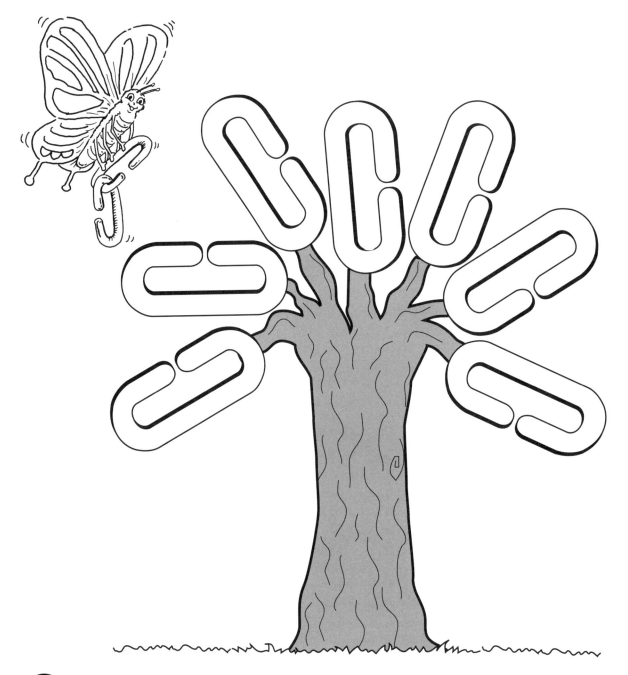

Link 'N' Learn® Activity Book
© Learning Resources, Inc.

Count Back

Place more than three bees (yellow links) on the bee hive. Write the number of bees (yellow links) in the first blank. Count back. Write the ending number in the second blank.

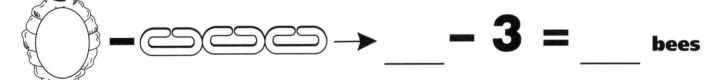

___ − **3** = ___ **bees**

___ − **3** = ___ **bees**

___ − **3** = ___ **bees**

Name _____ Date _____

Compare Red and Purple Links

Make the red and purple chains below. Subtract to find out how many more red or purple there is in each chain. Write number sentences in the blanks. Make two more red and purple chains on your own.

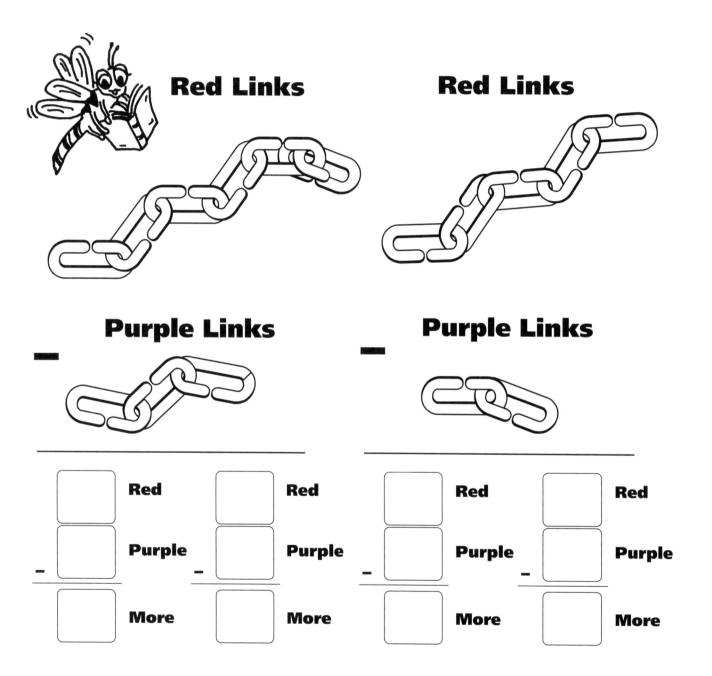

Red Links

Red Links

Purple Links

Purple Links

☐ Red ☐ Red ☐ Red ☐ Red

☐ Purple ☐ Purple ☐ Purple ☐ Purple

☐ More ☐ More ☐ More ☐ More

Name _____ Date _____

Check It Out

Make a train. Take some cars away. Then put them back. Write subtraction and the
 addition sentences.

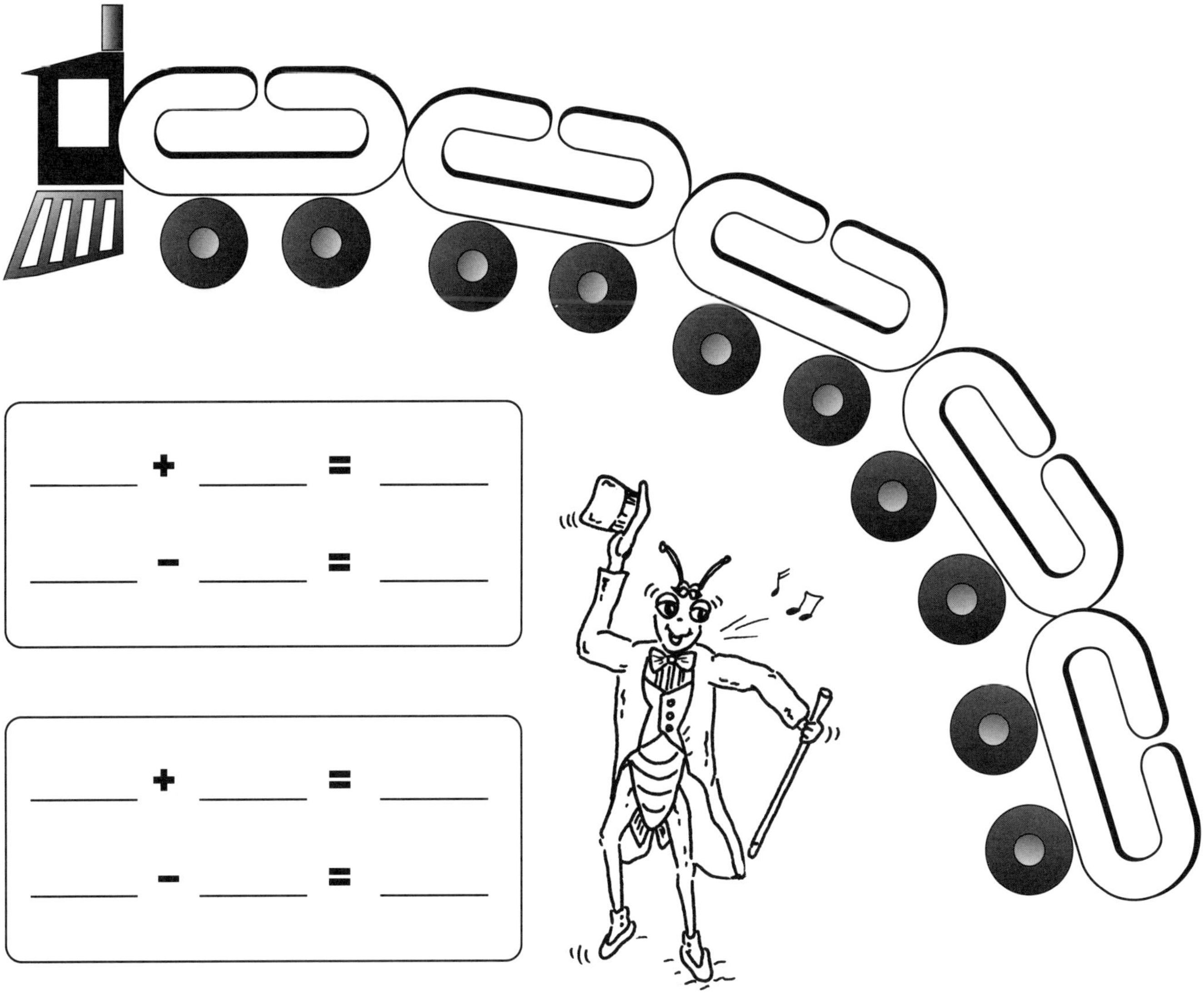

____ + ____ = ____

____ − ____ = ____

____ + ____ = ____

____ − ____ = ____

____ + ____ = ____

____ − ____ = ____

____ + ____ = ____

____ − ____ = ____

Name _____ **Date** _____

Take Away Some

Take away some ten-chains and some ones from a number. If there are not enough ones to subtract, break a ten.

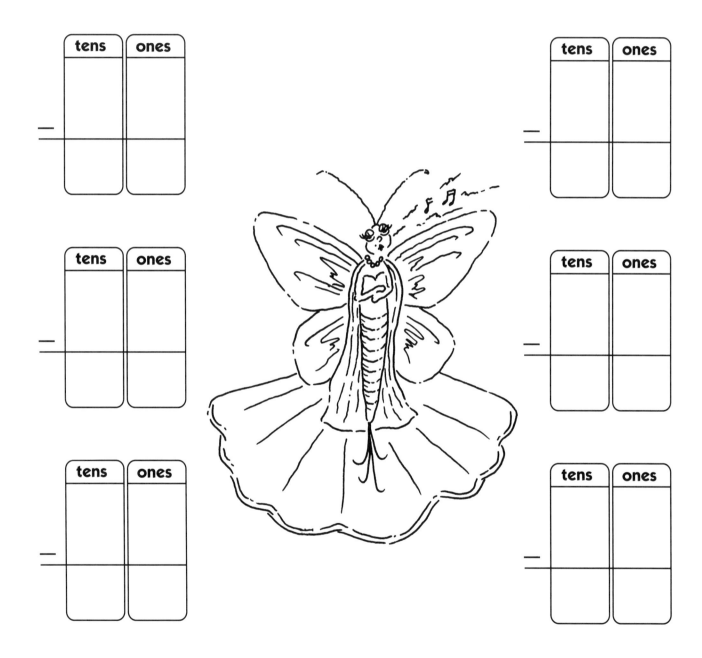

78

SECTION 9

Teaching Notes
Multiplication & Division

Page 81: Same to Each

Objective: Multiplication concept.

Getting Ready: Draw three mud piles on your chalkboard. Say: "Let your red links be worms. Show me four worms on the first mud pile. Show me four on the second pile, and four on the third. How many mud piles are there? (3) How many worms are on each pile? (4) There are three groups of four." Repeat this for other numbers of worms and mud piles.

Basic Activity: Encourage children to place worms (red links) on the mudpiles to model stories you tell. Example: "There were three mud piles with two worms on each. How many groups of two did you make?" Have children write a number sentence.

Extension: Write numbers sentences and challenge children to write stories to describe them.

Page 82: Turnarounds

Objective: Commutative property.

Getting Ready: Ask children to model the story with links. Bebe Bumblebee looked at her bug collection and said, "There are two rows of six beetles." Billi Bumblebee said, "I see six rows of two." Elicit number sentences.

Basic Activity: Children work with a partner to write number sentences, then write the turnaround.

Extension: Write a number sentence and challenge children to write the turnaround.

Page 83: Sharing Bugs

Objective: Division concept.

Getting Ready: Working in groups of three, children count and place 15 links in front of them. Say: "Give one link to each partner until all the links are passed out. Count the number of links you each have."

Basic Activity: Children use links as crickets and place them according to the story. "There were 16 crickets. We want to put the same number in each box. How many should we put in each box?" Encourage children to write a number sentence.

Extension: Write an expression and have children describe and model the sentence.

Page 84: Share Three Ways

Objective: Division with remainders.

Getting Ready: Select a dividend and a divisor that will yield a remainder. Ask children to sort and group their links with a pile for remainders.

Basic Activity: Children break apart links to form groups with remainders. Ask children to describe their groups and to tell how many links are remainders.

Extension: Increase the group size to four and repeat the above activity.

Page 85: Check It Out

Objective: Multiply to check division.

Getting Ready: Place 12 links on the overhead and divide them into three groups. Say: "We had twelve caterpillars and divided them into three groups. How many are in each group? (4) How many groups of four are there? (3) When we divide, we multiply to check."

Basic Activity: Children use links to divide and multiply to check.

Extension: Tape a division fact on the front of every child. Tape the multiplication on every child's back to check the division problem. Children have to solve the division problems with links then multiply to check. Encourage children to walk about and try problems taped to other children.

Link 'N' Learn® Activity Book
© Learning Resources, Inc.

Same to Each

Use links to match the story about worms.

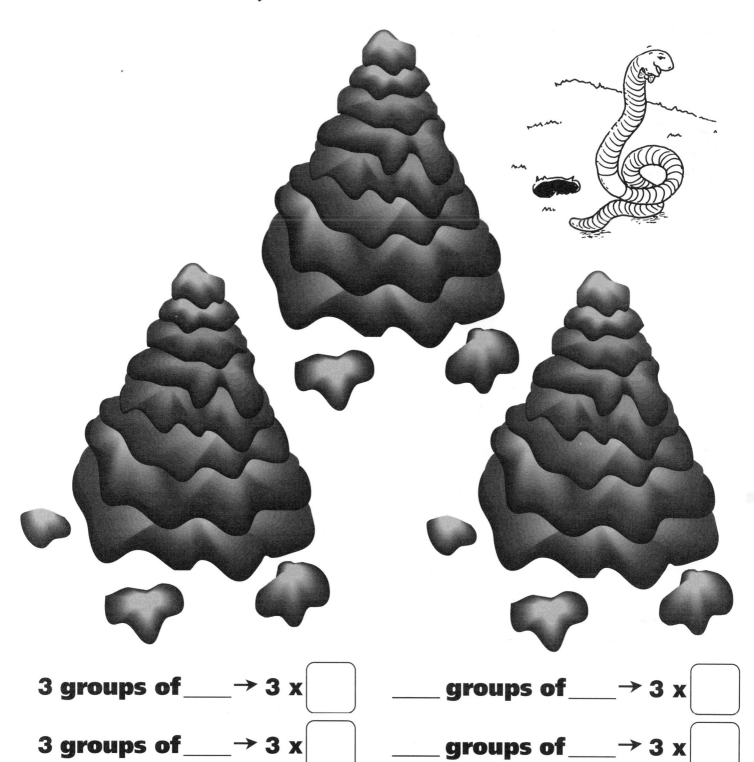

3 groups of _____ → **3 x** ▢   _____ **groups of** _____ → **3 x** ▢

3 groups of _____ → **3 x** ▢   _____ **groups of** _____ → **3 x** ▢

Name _____ Date _____

Turnarounds

Use links for dragonflies. Make rows of dragonflies for Bebe Bumblebee's bug collection. Write a multiplication sentence showing the product. Write another multiplication sentence describing the dragonflies.

Turnarounds		
Number of rows	Number in each row	Number in all
↓	↓	↓
___ (x) ___	(=) ___	
___ ◯ ___	◯ ___	

Turnarounds		
Number of rows	Number in each row	Number in all
↓	↓	↓
___ (x) ___	(=) ___	
___ ◯ ___	◯ ___	

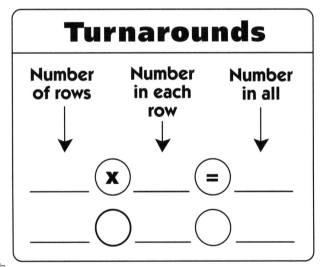

Name _____ **Date** _____

Sharing Bugs

Use links to match the story about crickets.

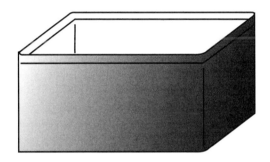

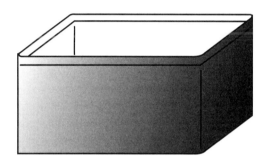

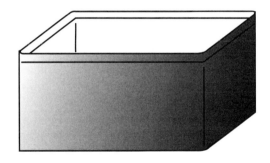

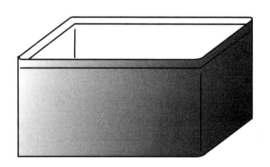

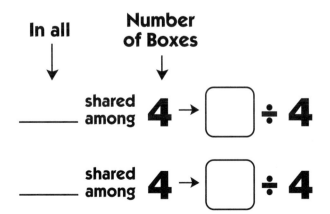

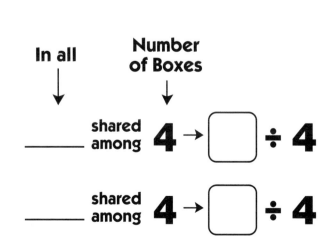

In all   Number of Boxes

____ shared among **4** → ☐ ÷ **4**

____ shared among **4** → ☐ ÷ **4**

In all   Number of Boxes

____ shared among **4** → ☐ ÷ **4**

____ shared among **4** → ☐ ÷ **4**

Share Three Ways

Make a chain. Count the links. Share it three ways. Keep track of leftovers in the table.

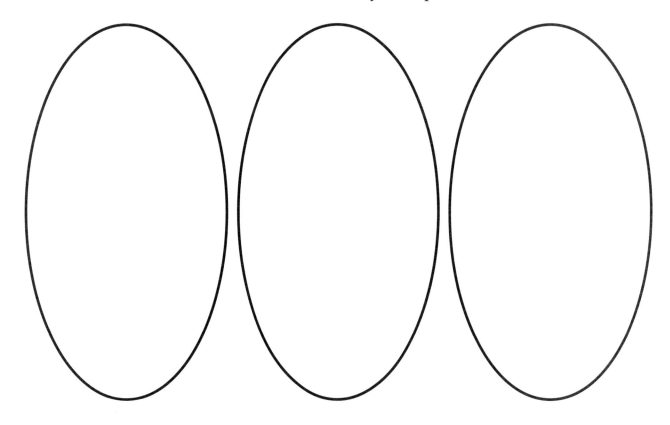

✔ the leftovers

Links at the start	0	1	2	3
6	✔			
7				
8				
9				
10				
11				

Is there a pattern?

_____

_____

_____

Check It Out

Use links to divide. Multiply with your links to check.

8 ÷ 2 = ____

____ x ____ = ____

9 ÷ 3 = ____

____ x ____ = ____

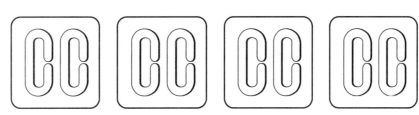

12 ÷ 4 = ____

____ x ____ = ____

10 ÷ 5 = ____

____ x ____ = ____

Link 'N' Learn® Activity Book
© Learning Resources, Inc.

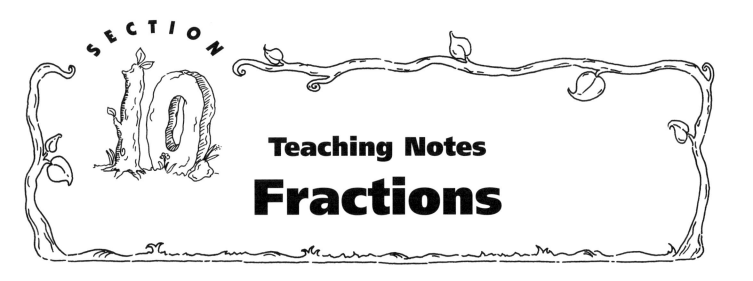

Teaching Notes
Fractions

Page 87: Part are Red

Objective: Fraction of a set.

Getting Ready: Children take a handful of links from a bag of red and orange links (substitute orange for yellow if using 4-color links). Encourage children to count the number of red and orange links in each handful they take.

Basic Activity: Children draw eight links from a bag of red and orange links (substitute with yellow if using 4-color links). Children write fractions to describe the number of red and orange links in each draw. For example: Three out of eight links are red.

Extension: Encourage children to make a link chain showing the fractions they pulled.

Page 88: Color a Chain

Objective: Fraction of a set.

Getting Ready: Children make blue and purple link chains (substitute blue for purple if using 4-color links) using three, four, or five links.

Basic Activity: Children record their link chains and write fractions to describe them. For example: Two of the five links are purple.

Extension: Children work in groups and make multicolor links. Children then challenge their peers to describe the fractions represented by certain colors.

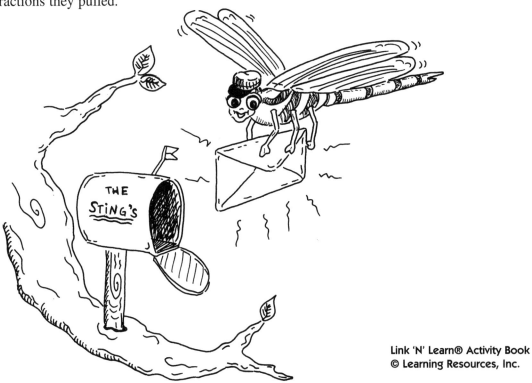

Link 'N' Learn® Activity Book
© Learning Resources, Inc.

Part are Red

Put red and orange links in a bag. Draw eight links from the bag. Record how many are red.

⬜ **of**
_____
⬜ **links are RED.**

⬜ **of**
_____
⬜ **links are RED.**

⬜ **of**
_____
⬜ **links are RED.**

Color a Chain

Make 2-color chains. Color the chains to match those you made. Write fractions describing your chains.

Link 'N' Learn® Activity Book
© Learning Resources, Inc.

Teaching Aids

Spinners

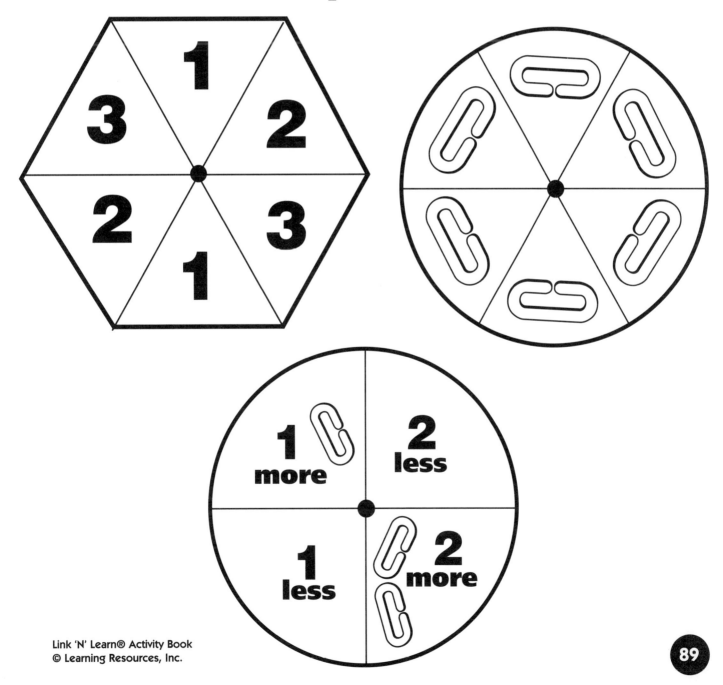

10-Frame

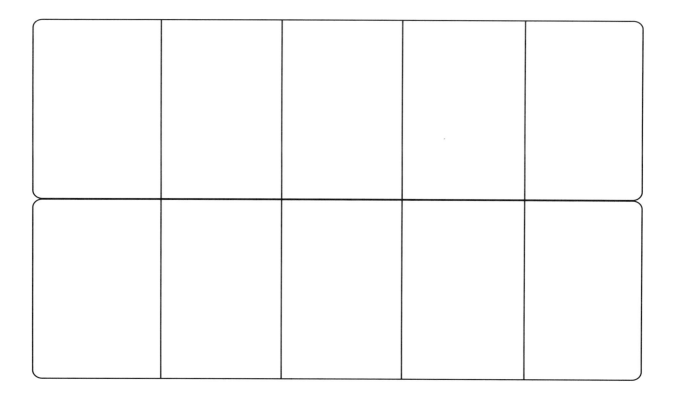

Link 'N' Learn® Activity Book
© Learning Resources, Inc.

Hundreds Chart and Peephole Puzzles

1	2	3	4	5	6	7	8	9	10
11	12	13	14	15	16	17	18	19	20
21	22	23	24	25	26	27	28	29	30
31	32	33	34	35	36	37	38	39	40
41	42	43	44	45	46	47	48	49	50
51	52	53	54	55	56	57	58	59	60
61	62	63	64	65	66	67	68	69	70
71	72	73	74	75	76	77	78	79	80
81	82	83	84	85	86	87	88	89	90
91	92	93	94	95	96	97	98	99	100

Peephole Puzzles

A.   **B.**

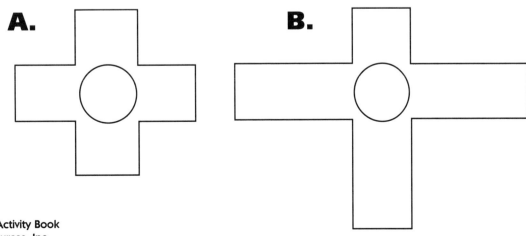

Large Links

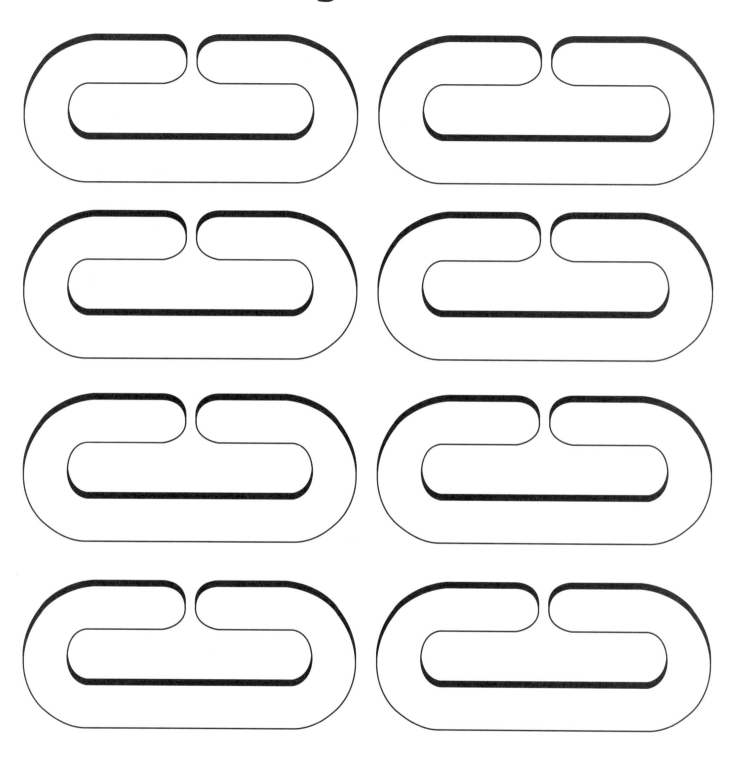

Link 'N' Learn® Activity Book
© Learning Resources, Inc.

Medium Links

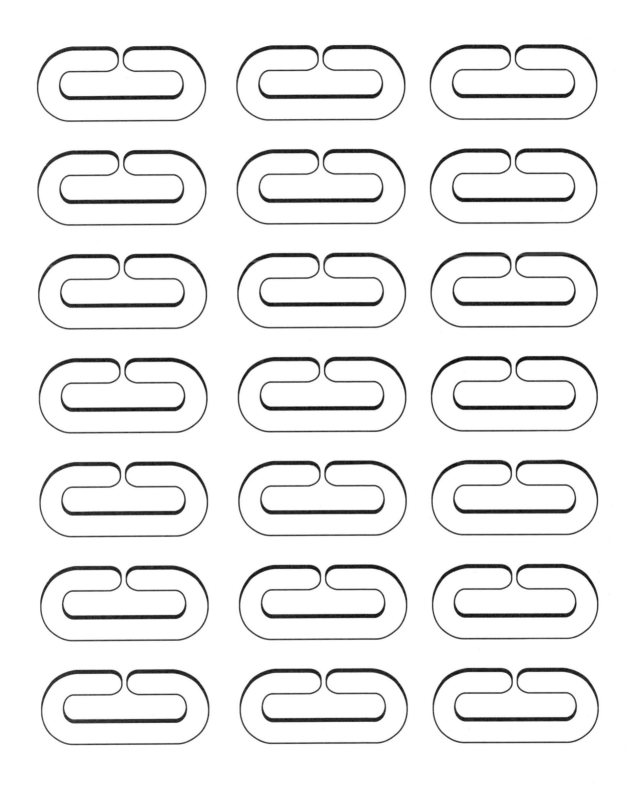

Small Links

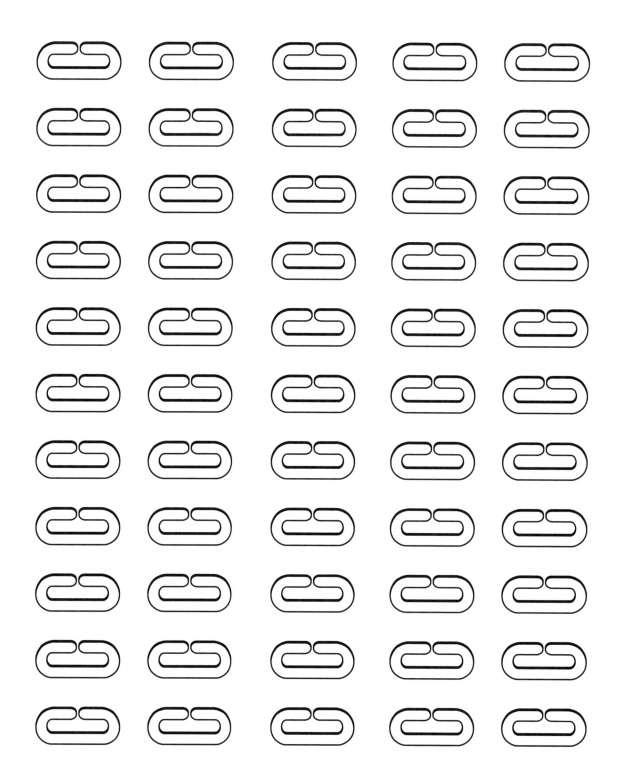

Link 'N' Learn® Activity Book
© Learning Resources, Inc.

Bibliography

Children's Literature Bibliography

- Bodecker, N. M. *Water Pennies and Other Poems*. New York: Margaret K. McElderry Books, 1991.

  Stop by the edge of a pond, and observe the abundance of life on and around the water. Animated poems explore the lifestyles of many different bugs with delicate pen-and-ink drawings.

- Carle, Eric. *The Grouchy Ladybug*. New York: T. Y. Crowell Co., 1977.

  A grouchy ladybug would rather fight than share her breakfast of aphids, then goes on to challenge everyone else she meets — only to return to where she started. In addition to learning about ladybugs, children become familiar with telling time, as clocks mark the hour of the ladybug's confrontations.

- Carle, Eric. *The Very Hungry Caterpillar*. New York: Philomel Books, 1969.

  Learn the days of the week and count to ten, as a very hungry caterpillar eats until he's stuffed, then retreats to his cocoon for a magnificent metamorphosis. Engaging collages and die-cut pages make this book a popular favorite.

- Carle, Eric. *The Very Quiet Cricket*. New York: Philomel Books, 1990.

  Repetitive text and large, colorful illustrations of insects introduce children to the cricket and his friends, as he tries to rub his wings and make a sound to say, "Hi."

- DeLuise, Dom. *Charlie the Caterpillar*. New York: Half Moon Books, 1990.

  Charlie the caterpillar is rejected by several groups of animal friends because of the way he looks. Then when he turns into a beautiful butterfly and meets another unhappy caterpillar, he discovers the meaning of true friendship.

- Farber, Norma. *Never Say Ugh to a Bug*. New York: Greenwillow Books, 1961.

  Animated illustrations and rhythmical lyrics bring children a special view of the creatures we generally regard as pests. Get advice from a water skater, or learn the mystery of the spider's web in this rousing collection of poems.

- Fisher, Aileen. ***When It Comes to Bugs***. New York: Harper & Row, 1986.

  Mrs. Beetle sets her alarm clock to escape the winter cold, and crickets chirp to count the stars. Children discover the magic of insects in this imaginative book of poems that looks at the world from a bug's point of view.

- Fowler, Richard. ***Ladybug on the Move***. New York: Doubleday, 1993.

  A ladybug is forced to leave her quiet corner in the garden when a hungry snail munches its way toward her home. This interactive book invites children to follow the ladybug's path with a separate piece that slips through the pages, bringing ladybug to realize there's no place like home.

- Joose, Barbara M. ***Spiders in the Fruit Cellar***. New York: Alfred A. Knopf, 1983.

  Little Elisabeth must face her fear of spiders when her mother asks her to go down to the cellar for a jar of peaches. When she drops the jar by accident, her mother reassures her it's okay to be afraid.

- Maxner, Joyce. ***Lady Bugatti***. New York: Lothrop, Lee & Shepard Books, 1991.

  Join Bupji Beetle, Dragonia Fly, Anatole Ant, Madame Flutterby, and Bumbly Bee on a magical excursion to dinner and a concert — as the guests of revered Madame Bugatti. Rhyming text and elegant illustrations help children see that bugs can be quite sophisticated!

- McNulty, Faith. ***The Lady and the Spider***. New York: Harper & Row, 1986.

  Children gain an appreciation of nature and life in this endearing book about a tiny spider who makes its home in the "caves" of a head of lettuce. When a lady finally harvests the head and destroys the spider's home, the spider must fight to stay alive — with a wonderfully heartwarming ending.

- Poulet, Virginia. ***Blue Bug's Book of Colors***. Chicago: Childrens Press, 1981.

  Blue Bug and his friends discover they can mix together different colors to make new colors — and in the process, they make a mess. Part of a series of "Blue Bug" books that both teach and entertain.

- Ryder, Joanne. ***Where Butterflies Grow***. New York: Lodestar Books, 1989.

  This beautifully illustrated book helps children imagine what it's like to be small, as they follow the dramatic transformation of a caterpillar into a black swallowtail butterfly. Includes instructions for raising butterflies in your garden.

- Trapani, Iza. ***The Itsy Bitsy Spider***. New York: Whispering Coyote Press, Inc., 1993.

  Children will laugh at the antics of a determined spider in this lively variation of the famous children's folksong, with beautifully rendered illustrations.

Link 'N' Learn® Activity Book
© Learning Resources, Inc.